Contents

Log Cabin Help

By

Nancy J. Nielsen

Illustrated by

Laurie Harden

Columbus, OH

SRAonline.com

 SRA

Chapter 1

On the Path to the School

*Ann, Ted, and Dan have left the log cabin. Now they go to the school.

Ted and Dan are big. They go fast. Ann can not go as fast.

Ann runs down the path to the school. She trips on a stump. Then she steps on her hem. She must get to the school.

It is cold. Ann grips her* hat. She needs Dan and Ted to help her.

Ann runs and runs. When will Ann see Dan and Ted?

Chapter 2

At the School

Dan and Ted can go faster than Ann. *They are at the school.

Ann gets to the school. The bell rings. Miss Green greets Ann. She asks Ann to sit down.

Ted and Dan are sitting in desks in the back of the school. Ann sits in her desk next to the flag.

"I will think. I will add. Six and six is 12," Ann says. She has* a math test.

"Now for the math test," Miss Green says. "You must add."

Ann has the test. Ted and Dan do not have it. They are older. They will read now.

Then Ted and Dan check the maps. They have ink pens. They fill in dots on maps on the desk.

Dan and Ted add a log to the fire. They all stop for lunch. The fire cracks. Ann sits by the fire. She is not cold now.

Chapter 3

Dinner at the Log Cabin

"Get the fork," Mom says. Ann gets the fork. She helps Mom get the food on the dish. They cut. They mash.

"Now we can have dinner," Mom says.

Dad steps in to the log cabin. Ted and Dan step in with him.

They sit down and have dinner.

"Ann helps," Mom says. "She gets things for me."

"Dan is a fixer," Dad says. "He can fix things with his hammer. He can set traps. Ted can chop wood. They help me."

"Yes, I can check the traps now," Dan says. "I think we will get a fox."

"Ted and Dan did not help me get to the school this morning," Ann says. "I need help."

"We will help Ann in the morning," Dan tells Mom and Dad.

They are happy.

*After dinner the lamp is lit.

"We got a letter from Sam in town," Mom says. "I will read the letter that Sam sent."

Then Ann gets the kit. Now Mom will mend Ann's hem.

The lamp is dim. Dad gets a log for the fire.

"We have a north wind," Dad says. "It will get colder. Then it will* snow."

Chapter 4

To the School in the Snow

It is colder in the morning. Snow is on the land. *It sits in the trees. It sits on top of the log cabin.

Ann gets her cap. She gets her mitts. Dan and Ted will help Ann get to the school.

Dan gets the sled. Ann sits on the sled. Dan and Ted pull the sled. They run fast. The sled slips up and down the hills on the path.* Ann has fun on the sled.

They get to the school. Ann gets her ink pen. Miss Green helps Ann. Ann is happy.

Snow is still dropping. After lunch Miss Green says that the snow is deep. She folds the flag.

"You must go home now," Miss Green says.

Chapter 5

The Steep Hill

*Ann gets her cap and her mitts. Dan and Ted tramp in the snow to get the sled. Ann sits on the sled. It is cold. The snow is deep.

"We can go up the steep hill," Ted says. "The sled will go so fast."

They go up the steep hill. Ann gets up. Ted sits on the sled. Ted* and the sled rush down the hill. Ted can not stop the sled.

"Ted will crash in to a tree!" Dan says.

Ted lands in the snow. He has a rip in his pants. He has a big gash on his leg.

"Help me!" Ted says. Dan will help Ted. Dan helps Ted get back on the sled.

"We will go now," Dan says.

It is cold. The snow is deep. Ann helps Ted. She tramps in the cold snow.

Dan and Ann help Ted get back to the log cabin.

Chapter 6

Ted Gets Better

Dan gets the sled back to the log cabin. Dad helps Ted get in bed. The gash is not bad.

*Ted can rest now. He will get better.

Ann helps Dad get a log for the fire. She helps Mom get a hot drink for Ted.

The sled has a dent in it. Dan gets the hammer. He will fix the sled.

"I wish I did not go down the steep hill," Ted says. "But I think I will get* better now."

"You did not help things," Dad says. "But Dan and Ann can help. The snow will stop. When you get better, you can go back to the school."